BART SIMPSON'S TREEHOUSE OF HORROR

HEEBIE-JEEBIE
HULLABALOO

HarperCollins*Entertainment*

An Imprint of HarperCollinsPublishers

IN LOVING MEMORY OF SNOWBALL I:
WHEREVER YOU ARE, WE HOPE THERE'S A WARM
SAUCER OF MILK FOR YOU...BUT NOT TOO WARM.

Published by HarperCollins*Entertainment* 1999

HarperCollins*Entertainment*
An Imprint of HarperCollins*Publishers*
77–85 Fulham Palace Road
London W6 8JB

www.harpercollins.co.uk

This edition produced for Premier Direct Group Plc in 2005

ISBN 0 00 771098 4

A catalogue record for this book is available from the British Library

Publisher
Matt Groening

Editor/Art Direction
Bill Morrison

Managing Editor
Terry Delegeane

Director of Operations
Robert Zaugh

Production/Design
Christopher Ungar and Karen Bates

Production Assistance
Chia-Hsien Jason Ho

Legal Guardian
Susan A. Grode

Contributing Writers
Mike Allred, Neil Alsip, Peter Bagge, Paul Dini, Evan Dorkin, Bill Morrison, James Robinson, and Jeff Smith

Contributing Artists
Mike Allred, Laura Allred, Alvin White Studio, Norm Auble, Karen Bates, Tim Bavington, Jeannine Crowell Black, Luis Escobar,
Stephanie Gladden, Chia-Hsien Jason Ho, Nathan Kane, James Lloyd, Bill Morrison, Robert Oliver, Phil Ortiz, Rhea Patton,
Julius Preite, Chris Roman, Aaron Rozenfeld, Mike Sakamoto, Jeff Smith, Steve Steere, Jr., and Christopher Ungar

HarperCollins Editors
Susan Weinberg, Trena Keating, and Susan Hoffner

Special thanks to:
Annette Andersen, Serban Cristescu, Claudia De La Roca, N. Vyolet Diaz, Deanna MacLellan, Mike Rote, and Mili Smythe

TABLE OF CONTENTS

ATTENTION EARTHLINGS!

Greetings. I am the one they call Matt Groening, and this is my sister, the one they call Kodos... Groening. It is possible you have seen me before and are saying to yourselves, "Yes, he looks like Matt Groening, but something has changed." As is customary in your entertainment sector, I have had my face sliced open and reattached to enhance my appearance. Anyway, I'm definitely not shoved under this desk in a Xanthor 5134-J radiation cooking device. While you admire my appealing new exterior, I will talk to you about this book, this Heebie-Jeebie Hullabaloo.

We humans love horror. It's why you chose this book from the dispensary rather than oh, say, Defending Your Planet From Intergalactic Space Aliens by Bill Moyers. DO NOT READ THIS MOYERS BOOK! For some reason, it is pleasing to be frightened. As a young pupa in Oregon, my favorite recreational implement was an earthling-in-a-box. If I would crank the handle long enough, an earthling impaled on a spring would leap forth from the box, screaming and gasping for air. Oh, how we would laugh with fear. This book should also make you laugh with fear, for it contains many interesting examples of earthling edu-tainment. Furthermore, it is chock full of your people's favorite form of communication — the advertisement. Read these well, for as with all ads, someone has gone to great pains to send subliminal messages about your impending doom.

Yes, the Heebie-Jeebie Hullabaloo is a book that will often make you frightened. But it is the kind of fright coupled with the joy of knowing it is just pretend and everything is going to be okay. And everything will be okay as long as you do not read the Moyers book. DO NOT READ THE MOYERS BOOK! We suggest you sit back, relax in your favorite place (perhaps far away from your personal firearms... perhaps in a large bowl of plum sauce), and enjoy Heebie-Jeebie Hullabaloo like it was the last book you will ever read.

END COMMUNICATION,

The One Known As Matt Groening

FROM CARL JUNG TO JOSEPH CAMPBELL, EXPERTS BELIEVE THAT DEEP IN THE HUMAN PSYCHE LIES A COMMON SET OF PRIMITIVE EMOTIONS PASSED ALONG SINCE THE DAWN OF MANKIND. AND MOST PRIMITIVE OF ALL IS THE SENSE OF FEAR. WITH THIS FEAR, CULTURES HAVE CREATED GHOST STORIES, TALES BASED ON A UNIVERSAL FORMULA SO POWERFUL, AN INDIVIDUAL COULD MERELY PLUG IN SOCIETAL SPECIFICS AND A GHOST STORY WOULD ARISE LIKE SMOKE FROM THE VERY CAULDRON OF TIME.

BASICALLY, LISA, HOMER, GRAMPA, AND I ARE EACH GONNA REWRITE THE SAME GHOST STORY. LIKE MAD-LIBS WITHOUT THE COPYRIGHT INFRINGEMENT.

BART!... WELL, YOU'RE RIGHT. BUT I GET TO GO FIRST!

THE CURSE OF THE THING!

As told by *Lisa Simpson*

When young *Vonda Marbury* agreed to go on the *bird-watching expedition* deep in the heart of *the Okefenokee Swamp*, she had no idea of the terror that would befall her on that fateful night.

Led by world-famous *birder, Victor LaPlante*, the group had traveled by *boat* to the deepest part of *the swamp* to find *a rare bird called the black-crested gratch*. Coming around a bend, *Vonda* spied an old man *on the shore*. "Stay away from *Death's Head Cave*, for that is the home of *Caucohotec*." *Vonda* had heard this myth. Long ago, *Chief Caucohotec* had been *burned alive and eaten* by a rival *tribe*. Before he died, he swore his ghost would seek vengeance. Anyone he caught would *be burned and eaten as he had been*. But *Vonda* couldn't worry about myths. To find the *black-crested gratch*, they had to go to *Death's Head Cave*. As they left, they could hear the old man mutter, "*Caucohotec, tonight you shall be fed*."

Because members of the group were scared, *Victor* agreed to sit up all night with his gun. "*See you tomorrow at breakfast*," he joked, "*unless I'm Caucohotec's dinner!*" Later that night, young *Vonda* was awoken by gunshots followed by a hideous scream. She ran to the spot where *Victor* had been. Instead she found his *broken rifle* and a *patch of scorched earth from a recent bonfire*. Suddenly, she heard a rustle in the bushes. THUMP, THUMP, SCRAPE... THUMP, THUMP, SCRAPE! Was it *Caucohotec*?! *Vonda* began running back through the inky darkness toward *the boat*. Once she reached it, she'd motor back to civilization and send for help. It seemed like an eternity, but she finally found it. Her passage to safety! And as if that weren't enough, there *on the prow of the boat* she could make out *a black crest of feathers*... She'd actually found *the black-crested gratch*! But as she got closer, she realized *the shadow of the bird* was much bigger than she had imagined. Could it be *the black crest* was actually *the feathers of an Indian headdress*?

That morning in the *Okefenokee* Gazette there was a short article near the back: "*Birding Expedition Missing, Feared Drowned*." An old man put down the paper and muttered to himself, "*Caucohotec has been sated*."

:SNIFF!:

:COUGH!:

INFIRMARY

:KAA-CHOO!: **BLAST** THIS COLD. RIGHT NOW I'D **KILL** FOR A DRAM OF NYQUIL.

OKAY, TERWILLIGER, YOU KNOW THE DEAL. BECAUSE YOU **VOLUNTEERED** FOR THIS **FOOLHARDY** AND ALMOST CERTAINLY **LIFE-THREATENING** EXPERIMENT, WE'RE CUTTING YOUR PRISON TIME IN **HALF.**

:SNIFF!: WARDEN, I'M ANXIOUS TO COOPERATE IN ANY WAY THAT WILL ALLOW ME TO GET OUT EARLY AND RESUME MY **TRUE AVOCATION**...

AAUUGHH!

...HELPING OIL-SOAKED SEA BIRDS **RETURN** TO THEIR **NATURAL ENVIRONMENT.**

:AAA-CHOOO!:

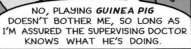

NO, PLAYING **GUINEA PIG** DOESN'T BOTHER ME, SO LONG AS I'M ASSURED THE SUPERVISING DOCTOR KNOWS WHAT HE'S DOING.

HI, EVERYBODY!

HI, DR. NICK!

:SNIFF!: ON SECOND THOUGHT, YOU MAY **RETURN** ME TO "THE HOLE."

GRRRAAAHHHH!

WHOA, SILLY ME! I GOTTA THE *FORMULA REVERSED!* WHADDA YA THINK ABOUT THAT?

SMACK!

I THINK IT'S TIME TO SAY...

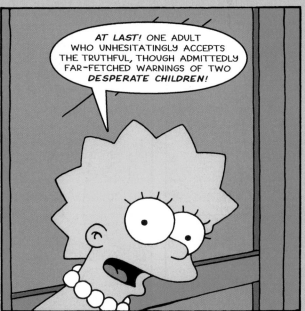

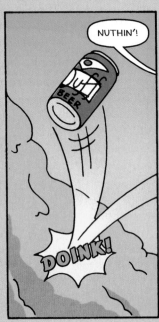

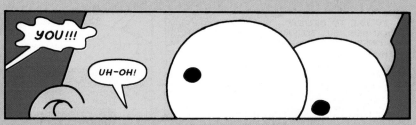

Jiggle when you giggle?
Rumble when you tumble?
Time to lose that extra weight! Time for...

KangFast!®

Magic Shrinking Granules

KangFast!® is not a cunning plan to introduce muscle-weakening hormones into the populace in order to make humans slower targets, nor is it an internal spicing mechanism to make humans tastier. It's the revolutionary fat-obliteration formula that will make you a newer you.

Just listen to these candid testimonials...

Kodos: Housewife, Mother of Two:

"After I expelled my second infant, Porgatz the Malevolent, I became slow and less attractive to future mating partners. When I would go to the purchasing complex, other humans would laugh and throw sun-ripened comestibles in my direction. I decided it was time for KangFast! In just three lunar rotations, I eliminated one third of my molecular mass. Now, when I go to the purchasing complex, I'm the one throwing the sun-ripened comestibles!"

Kang: Sun-ripened Comestibles Salesman:

"When I received the communication alerting me to my educational reunion, my gelatinous sides quivered in fear. The other educatees would stare in scorn at my expanded girth. Perhaps they would poke at my abdomen wondering if I was about to expel an infant. I even tried to fit into my old athletics garment, but as soon as I moved, it blew into bits. 'I shall begin KangFast!' I announced. By the time I went to my educational reunion, I had become so small, nobody recognized me! Not only was I not mocked, I was able to anonymously abscond with great amounts of valuable booty."

Many say to exercise. DO NOT!! Your stringy gristle is our wasted meat.

The KangFast! regimen is easy: Have a shake for breakfast, a shake for lunch, and be ~~eaten as~~ be eating a sensible dinner.

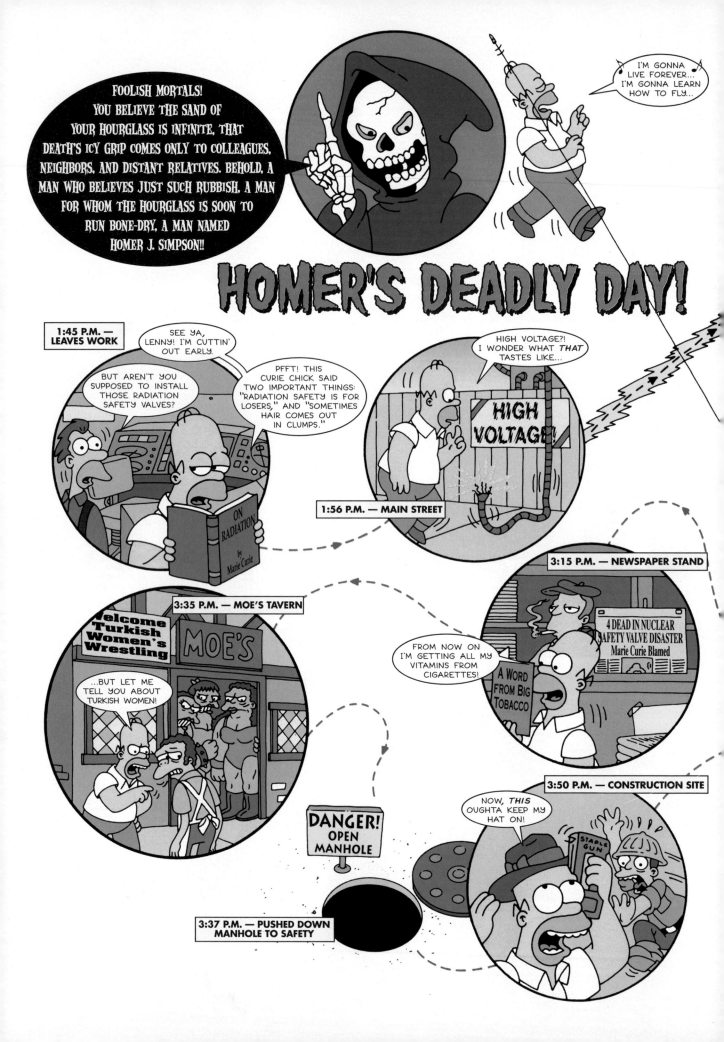

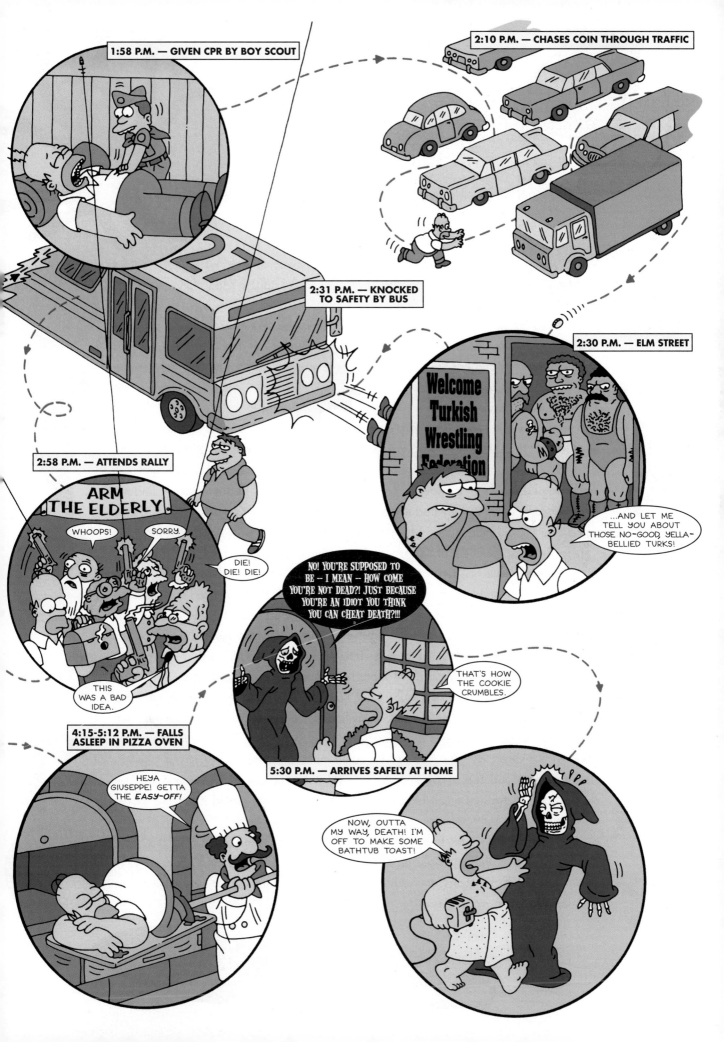

MEDICAL EXPERTS AGREE: MY SISTER'S A WIENER. LET ME SHOW YOU HOW TO TELL A *REAL* GHOST STORY!

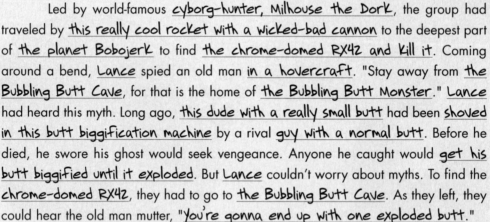

THE CURSE OF THE THING!

As told by Bart Simpson

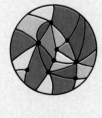

When young Star Capt. Lance Rapley agreed to go on the the cyborg-killing mission deep in the heart of the Fromzorb Nebula, he had no idea of the terror that would befall him on that fateful night.

Led by world-famous cyborg-hunter, Milhouse the Dork, the group had traveled by this really cool rocket with a wicked-bad cannon to the deepest part of the planet Bobojerk to find the chrome-domed RX42 and kill it. Coming around a bend, Lance spied an old man in a hovercraft. "Stay away from the Bubbling Butt Cave, for that is the home of the Bubbling Butt Monster." Lance had heard this myth. Long ago, this dude with a really small butt had been shoved in this butt biggification machine by a rival guy with a normal butt. Before he died, he swore his ghost would seek vengeance. Anyone he caught would get his butt biggified until it exploded. But Lance couldn't worry about myths. To find the chrome-domed RX42, they had to go to the Bubbling Butt Cave. As they left, they could hear the old man mutter, "You're gonna end up with one exploded butt."

Because members of the group were scared, Milhouse the Dork agreed to sit up all night with his gun. "See you tomorrow," he joked, "No ifs, ands or butts!" Later that night, young Lance was awoken by gunshots followed by a hideous scream. He ran to the spot where Milhouse the Dork had been. Instead he found his melted plasma ray and a pair of tightie-whities with the back ripped open. Suddenly, he heard a rustle in the bushes. THUMP, THUMP, SCRAPE... THUMP, THUMP, SCRAPE! Was it the Bubbling Butt Monster?! Lance began running back through the inky darkness toward the really cool rocket with the wicked-bad cannon. Once he reached it, he'd motor back to civilization and send for help. It seemed like an eternity, but he finally found it. His passage to safety! And as if that weren't enough, there in the door of the rocket he could make out a big shiny round thing... He'd actually found the chrome-domed RX42! But as he got closer, he realized the shiny round thing was much bigger than he had imagined. Could it be the dome was actually the butt side of the Bubbling Butt Monster?

That morning in the Fromzorb Gazette there was a short article near the back: "RX42 Destroys Planet Bobojerk Because RX42 Hunters Had Their Butts Blown Up By Butt Monster." An old man put down the paper and muttered to himself, "I am one oooold man!"

33

LATER...

ACCORDING TO ALL THE TESTS, AND BASED ON MY KNOWLEDGE AND YEARS OF EXPERIENCE, I AM FORCED TO CONCLUDE THAT THERE IS *ABSOLUTELY NOTHING WRONG* WITH YOUR CHILD, MRS. SIMPSON!

BUT *LOOK* AT HER, DOCTOR! LOOK AT WHAT SHE'S DOING WITH HER HANDS! YOU CALL THAT *NORMAL*?!?

THAT'S A PHENOMENON WE REFER TO AS "VOGUING"-- A SYMPTOM THAT WAS VERY MUCH ;AHEM!; IN VOGUE A FEW YEARS BACK. I'M SURPRISED TO SEE IT'S STILL AROUND...

MY GOODNESS! IS IT *CONTAGIOUS*?

BRIAN MOS
PATIENT ID# 666

THANKFULLY, NO. SHE SHOULD GET OVER IT IN A FEW DAYS. LORD KNOWS EVERYBODY ELSE HAS... MY RECEPTIONIST WILL DISCUSS MY BILL WITH YOU. GOOD DAY.

HMMM...MAYBE I SHOULD GET A *SECOND OPINION*...

LATER STILL...

DR. MONROE'S THERAPY TO GO

THERE'S NO DOUBT ABOUT IT, MRS. SIMPSON--YOUR DAUGHTER IS DEFINITELY SUFFERING FROM ALZHEIMER'S DISEASE!

ALZHEIMER'S?!? BUT SHE'S ONLY EIGHT YEARS OLD!

OH, UH, DID I SAY ALZHEIMER'S? WHAT I MEANT TO SAY WAS, ER... ATTENTION DEFICIT DISORDER! YEAH, THAT'S IT, GOOD OL' *ADD*!...BROUGHT ON BY COMPLICATIONS ASSOCIATED WITH, UH... *MENOPAUSE*!

GOOD GRIEF! NOBODY HAS A CLUE WHAT'S WRONG WITH MY POOR LISA! I'M STARTING TO GET *DESPERATE*!

♪ ...WE ARE LIVING IN A MATERIAL WORLD, AND I AM A MATERIAL GIRL... ♪

...GET OFF OUR FREAKIN' BACKS, YA BUNCHA UPTIGHT, NO FUN, GOODY TWO-SHOES YA--

THANK YOU, MR. KRUSTY, FOR THOSE WELL-CHOSEN WORDS.

I'M SURE THAT THE GOOD PEOPLE AT BUZZ COLA WILL BE GLAD TO LEARN THAT OUR BOYCOTT IS OFFICIALLY OVER. AND NOW ON TO OUR NEXT TOPIC...

CLAP CLAP

ONE HOUR LATER...

EXCUSE ME, MA'AM, BUT THE MEETING IS OVER... CAN I HELP YOU WITH ANYTHING, MISS...

...MRS. SIMPSON?!?

I HAVE TO TALK TO YOU, REVEREND.

AND SO...I'M AT MY WIT'S END, REVEREND, AND I DON'T KNOW WHAT ELSE TO DO, SO I'M TURNING TO YOU FOR HELP.

B-BUT, MRS. SIMPSON, YOU CAN'T REALLY BELIEVE THAT YOUR DAUGHTER IS POSSESSED BY THE SPIRIT OF MADONNA! I MEAN, LET'S GET REAL HERE; MS. CICCONE IS STILL ALIVE...I THINK.

DON'T TELL ME YOU DON'T BELIEVE ME EITHER! I THOUGHT FOR SURE AFTER THE WAY YOU WERE TALKING AT THE BARBECUE THAT--

OH, THAT. ⊡HEH-HEH!⊡ I'M AFRAID THAT WAS JUST THE BLOODY MARYS TALKING...

WE MINISTERS JUST CAN'T RESIST BREAKING INTO OUR FIRE-AND-BRIMSTONE ROUTINE FROM TIME TO TIME...

I SEE... WELL, I GUESS I SHOULD HAVE GONE TO SEE THE CATHOLIC PRIEST IN THE FIRST PLACE...

W-WHOA, NOW, MRS. SIMPSON, LET'S NOT BE HASTY!

IT'S TRUE THAT MY DENOMINATION DOESN'T BELIEVE IN EXORCISM, BUT WHO KNOWS, THIS MAY TURN OUT TO BE A GREAT NEW SOURCE OF REVENUE FOR THE CHURCH!

THAT NIGHT...

...EMIT TSRIF YREV EHT ROF DEHCUOT--ABMOOB ABMOOB ABMOOB-- NIGRIV A EKIL...

THANK GOODNESS YOU'RE HERE, REVEREND!

YEAH, AND NOT A MOMENT TOO SOON! I CAN'T HEAR THE TV!

WELL, I MIGHT AS WELL GET RIGHT DOWN TO BUSINESS.

IF YOU CAN'T CURE HER, REV, COULD YOU AT LEAST GET HER TO *EXPAND HER REPERTOIRE*?

AND THE BIG GAME STARTS IN ONE HOUR, SO TRY TO MAKE IT SNAPPY!

⁞GULP⁞ THIS IS IT! I HOPE I...WAIT, WHAT'S THIS?

EXORCIST UTILITY BELT

NO ONE SAID ANYTHING ABOUT A...OH, WHAT AM I *SAYING*?

MUST HAVE VIP PASS TO ENTER BACKSTAGE

BAM!

GOOD LORD! ⁞CHOKE⁞

THE END.

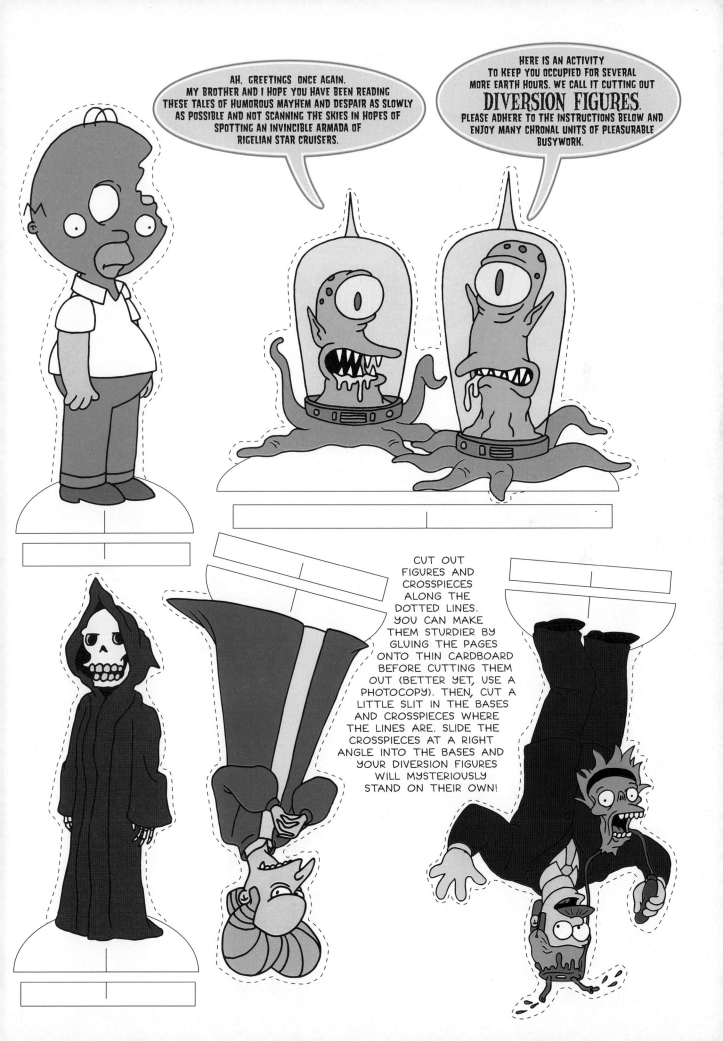

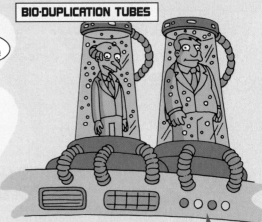

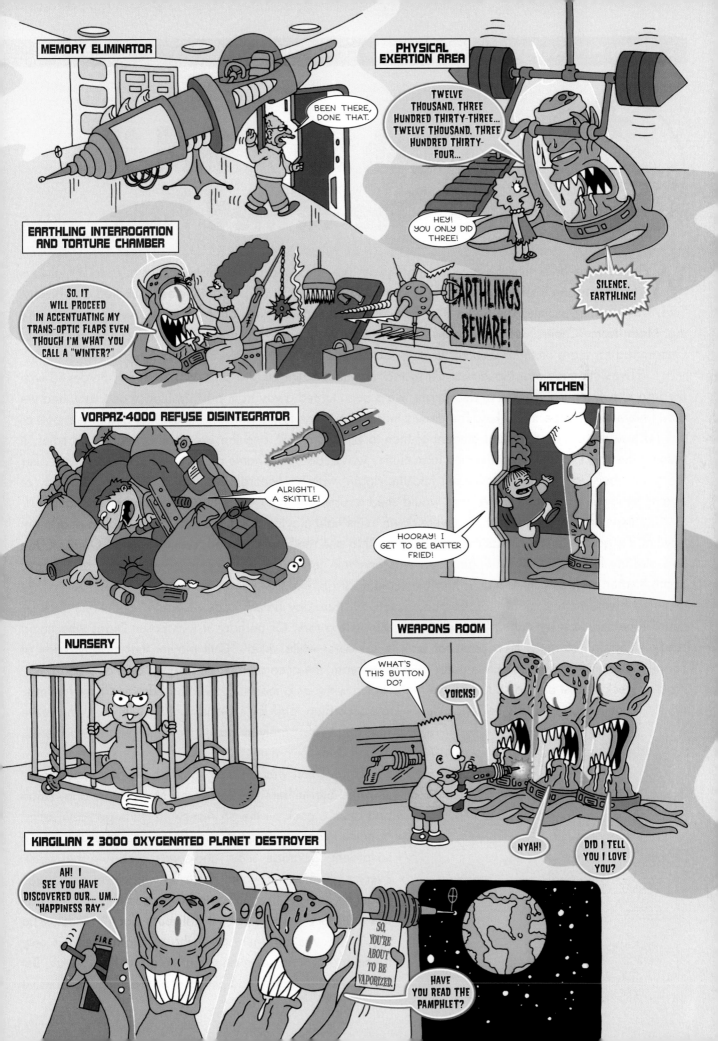

"MANY TALES THERE BE, WRIT IN BLOOD ON THE SEA..."

Elijah Dunn and the One-Armed Nun

When I peer back through my life, most years are shrouded in the mists of memory. But I'll always remember one fateful year like it was yesterday. The Year of Our Lord Nineteen Hundred and Ninety-Two. 'Twas a simpler time. The Berlin Wall had fallen, the economy was on the rise, and everyone was sure that Norm from "Cheers" would have his own hit show. Truly a time of sunshine and innocence. But Mother Ocean had far more ominous weather in store for me and the ill-fated crew of the SS *Natalie Wood*.

'Twas the middle of November. At sea for six months, we were a ship with no home. Burdened with a cargo of two thousand sticks of deodorant, we'd been turned away from ports in France and Italy, and we didn't have much hope for Turkey. The crew's morale had sunk to the bottom. I knew that at the next port o' call I'd lose more than the usual amount of men to bars, brothels, and the siren call of real estate sales. It seemed the only thing that kept the men from mutiny was a lad by the name of Hornpipe Joe. Every night after the dinner bell, Joe would hoist himself into the riggin' with his accordion and play a version of "Lady of Spain" so lovely even Ironeye Williams would shed a rusty tear. But that night, everything would change.

'Twas nine bells and most of us were down in the hold playing a game we'd invented called deodorant bowlin'. I'd been winnin', but as the saying goes, "No one really wins in deodorant bowlin'." On deck, Joe had already finished "Lady of Spain" and was beginnin' a longer, more complicated version of "Lady of Spain," when suddenly there was a horrible scream, arrgh, like the wail of the banshee herself. At first we assumed it was nothin' more than Barnaby Tench. Ol' Barnaby hated "Lady of Spain" and every time he heard it he'd protest by stabbin' himself in the shin with a fork. Or perhaps it was Bosun Diggs who hated "Lady of Spain" so much he'd pour hot wax in his ears, while yellin' "Quit playin' that crappy 'Lady of Spain!'" But this scream was different, for after this scream, the accordion music stopped cold as a heartbeat. I ran on deck as fast as I could to find the night watch white as a mainsail, the blood drained from his face. Slowly he held aloft a gruesome spectacle — Joe's accordion, and Joe's bloody shirt... with the right sleeve

missing. With barely a gasp, the night watch whispered, "Elijah Dunn!"

Elijah Dunn was a name known by all mariners, and it shivered our timbers like wet wool. Many years ago, Elijah had been a cook on the SS *Agnew*, a garbage scow sailin' from the mighty garbage mines of Newark. Of all the jobs in sailordom, garbage scow cook was probably the worst. Every night the men would come up with clever new barbs about his cookin', like "What is this garbage?" and "You call this Salisbury steak? I calls it Salisbury boot!" Needless to say, Elijah was an ornery cuss who kept to himself, his only friend a parrot named Arthur that he'd taught to speak. But Arthur was a drunk, and theirs soon became an abusive relationship that ended in tears. By year's end, Elijah's heart was a barnacle-covered hull at the bottom of the ocean, a heart that could only be salvaged by the romance of a beautiful woman. And that woman would be Sister Mary Catherine, the one-armed nun.

She came aboard on Staten Island, headed east to the Hamptons on a mission to minister to the nearly unwealthy. Aye, she was a beauty! Broad of beam, stout of chest and dressed head-to-toe in luxuriant, form-concealin' black. But like the most radiant diamond, she had one minor flaw. She was missing an arm, lost during her days as a competitive lumberjack. But that was a minor flaw indeed for as soon as she stepped on deck, Elijah's heart leapt up from the very depth of his core. That afternoon, Elijah went all-out preparin' the evening meal. Even the crew was astounded, praisin' that the food had decreased in stench by at least twenty percent, maybe twenty-two. But Elijah saved the sweetest morsel for dessert. At that moment he announced that by the end of the night, he would take Mary Catherine's one good hand in the holy vow of marriage. The room sat stunned for what seemed like an eternity until Mary Catherine finally stood up and decried in tones clear as a clarion bell, "No, you nitwit, I'm a nun!"

But Elijah stood his ground, "Do not let society's cruel gaze wither our love! I know you have but one arm, and it matters not! For how many arms are needed for a kiss? How many arms does it take to share a soul?!" At which someone from the crowd was moved to declare, "Yo, looney tunes, she's a nun!" But Elijah would not be deterred. He grabbed Mary Catherine and rushed her out on deck where the Captain was enjoyin' the night air. Elijah's heart sang with passion, "We know our romance will be spurned by the nattering nabobs and militant 'two-armers' on the boat, but surely you as captain can see we must be conjoined in the holiest of matrimonies!" The Captain took a long pensive draw on his pipe and then replied, "Are you on goofballs? 'Cause if you are, I don't want you handlin' the can opener." This was the last straw for the star-crossed lover. Elijah stood atop the railin', cryin', "Come with me, my one true love, and we shall be married by the sea herself in the home of the eight-armed octopus and the no-armed eel, a place where arms do not matter, only love!... You are comin' with me, right?" Mary Catherine shook her head. "Well, then help me get down." But it was too late. For at that very moment, Elijah slipped and fell off the rail and as he fell, he called out, "Don't worry my sweet! I shall avenge your despair! Two-armers shall pay for our lost looooove!" And with a splash, he was gone. Well, he wasn't quite gone, he was flounderin' in the water behind the boat, but unfortunately it was at this very time the scow chose to dump its garbage.

And now, out in the middle of the Mediterranean, Elijah's gruesome revenge had come to pass. We searched fore and aft for young Hornpipe Joe, but found not a stitch of clothes, not a drop of blood. And all the while, despite our efforts, we knew in our hearts that Joe had been snatched away into the deepenin' fog of the Other Side, earthly payment for the spirit of lost love. And to this day, when the ocean breeze lies still and the air hangs tight like a winter coat, I remember Joe and his accordion and his endless versions of "Lady of Spain" playin' over and over and over, and I think, "Thank God he's dead."

Kangboro

Welcome to My Flavor Trap

When your puny sun has set and the hours of labor have ceased, you may then enjoy the smooth taste of a Kangboro soot-inhaling tube. Sitting around a flame-hole, gazing up at the stars, you can relax in your ignorance of a planet known as Rigel-4 and the violent devastation its inhabitants are preparing to inflict upon you. Within a matter of solar days, your people will be running around, their heads aflame like so many soot-inhaling tubes, screaming that they are in flavor country. But now is not the time to prepare for the upcoming apocalypse.

Now is **your** time.

54

The **IMMIGRATION** of the **BODY SNATCHERS!**

THAT MAY BE TRUE, BUT NO ONE HAS EVEN COME TO TRY OUT MY NEWLY INSTALLED KIDDIE BALL PIT AND TUBE PLAYGROUND!

OOOOH...CAN I TRY IT?

NO, MR. HOMER, I AM SORRY, BUT YOU ARE FAR TOO FAT AND FUDGY FOR MY TINY TYKE HABITRAIL.

HUH! I BET YOU'VE TRIED IT!

OH YES, THAT IS ONE OF MY MANY PRIVILEGES AS OWNER AND OPERATOR OF THIS ESTABLISHMENT.

IT IS HOURS OF FUN, I MIGHT ADD.

"BITTER WITH DISAPPOINTMENT, I RETURNED HOME--."

HOMER! BUT--

YES, MARGE, I'M HOME EARLY. AND NO I DON'T WANNA DISCUSS IT BECAUSE I DIDN'T SCREW ANYTHING UP. I JUST FELT LIKE COMING HOME EARLY AND NOT ENJOYING MY DAY, OKAY?!

HI KIDS. WHAT'S UP?

NOTHING, HOMER. NONE OF OUR FRIENDS WANT TO PLAY OR RIDE BIKES OR DO ANYTHING! IT'S A TOTAL BUMMER!

THE WHOLE TOWN'S QUIET... TOO QUIET, I'D SAY.

IT APPEARS OUR GENERATION IS SADLY APPROACHING ADULTHOOD, WITH ITS ATTENDANT SLOTH AND LETHARGY.

≥YAWN≤ WELL, GUESS I'LL GET A JUMP ON ADULTHOOD WITH MY FIRST POST-INFANT NAP.

BRIIIING

A NAP? SAY, THAT'S A GOOD--

YYYELLO? WHAT? AN EMERGENCY? CAN'T YOU CALL THE COPS? OH, ALRIGHT-- I'LL BE RIGHT OVER!

57

"IT WAS AN *EMERGENCY CALL* FROM MY GOOD FRIEND, *BARNEY GUMBLE!* I RUSHED OVER *IMMEDIATELY*--"

HOMER, AREN'T YOU GOING OVER TO HELP BARNEY?

HUH? OH, YEAH, YEAH...I'M GOIN'...

"I WAS PROUD BARNEY CALLED ME, CONSIDERING HOW MANY COMPETENT PEOPLE THERE WERE IN TOWN."

OH, HI HOMER, DID I CALL YOU? I THOUGHT I CALLED "*HARD COPY*." OH WELL, COME ON IN, I'LL SHOW YA SUMTHIN'!!

LAST NIGHT I PASSED OUT BACK HERE AFTER A PARTICULARLY INTRIGUING INSTALLMENT OF "*BAYWATCH NIGHTS*". THEN WHEN I WOKE UP THIS AFTERNOON--

CLUNK

K-DUNK

CLUNK

--I FOUND THIS *THING* GROWING NEXT TA ME!

BARNEY...IT'S LIKE SOME KINDA GIGANTIC *POD*--WITH *YOUR HEAD ON IT!*

YEAH, PRETTY GOOD LIKENESS, HUH?

HEY! THERE'S A BIG *BITE* TAKEN OUT OF IT!

YEAH, WELL, I GOT KINDA *HUNGRY*, SO I FIGURED I'D TRY IT.

HMMM. HOW'D IT TASTE?

UHH...KINDA *FAMILIAR*.

61

65

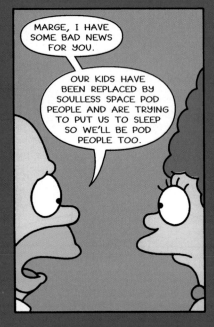

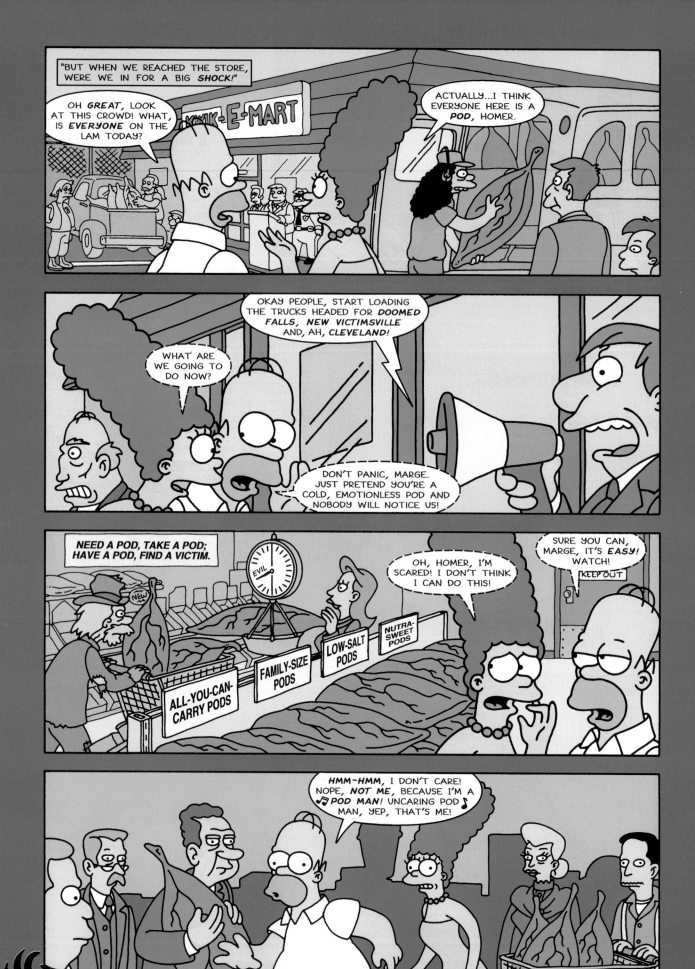

71

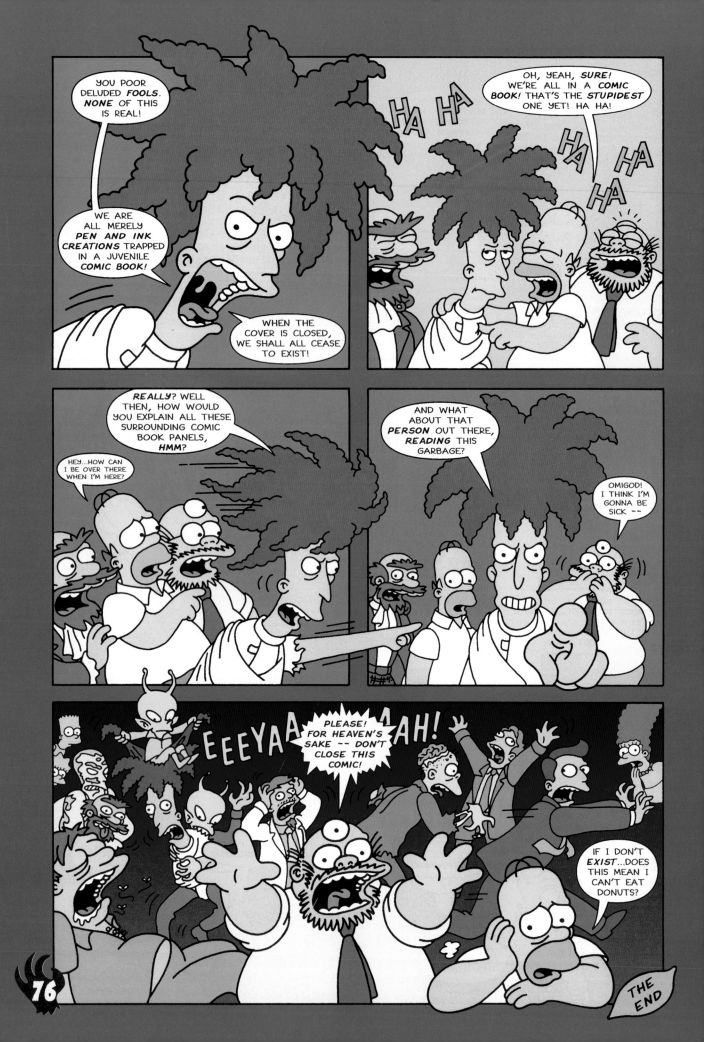

In High School, They Expected to Find
Good Times, Wild Parties, and Infant-Eating Contests.
What They Didn't Expect to Find...
Was Love.

Teen Superstar Kangy in...

Underage Comedy Hijinks II:

The Continuance of Underage Comedy Hijinks.

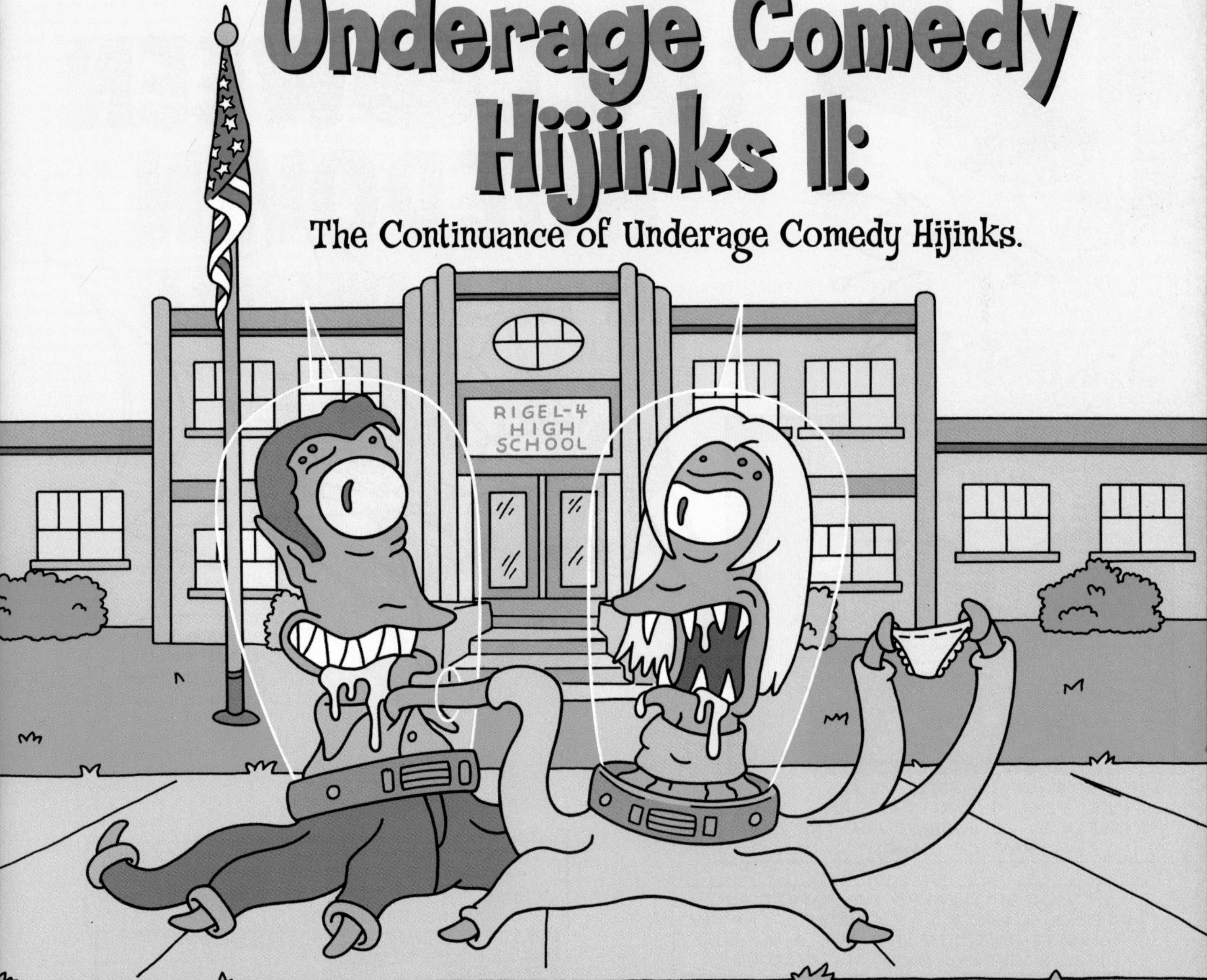

"You'll love Kangy when you realize he's not an old person!"
— ***Movie Minute***

"I enjoyed Kodos' surgically expanded thorax!"
– Gene Shalit

"This film is clearly not designed to divert attention from the intergalactic star destroyer focusing its detonation ray at the Earth's core."
— ***Newsday***

RIGEL-4 PRESENTS A SERAC THE PREPARER FILM "UNDERAGE COMEDY HIJINKS II" STARRING KANGY KODOS AND LYLE WAGGONER MUSIC BY OSMUTH THE CACOPHONOUS COSTUMES DESIGNED BY MR. KRONK OF XANTIBAR 9 EDITED BY A GIANT MACHINE SCREENPLAY BY THRANK THE REDUNDANT BASED ON THE NOVELLA BY STEPHEN KING EXECUTIVE PRODUCER THE ALL-KNOWING ORB: ALL HAIL THE ALL-KNOWING ORB AND HIS MERCILESS BRAND OF INFOTAINMENT

R	This film is strictly for adults only.
	Leave the children at home. Preferably on the doorstep, preferably marinating.

HOWDY, NEIGHBOR! OR SHOULD I SAY "NEIGH-BOO!" EVERY YEAR AT HALLOWEEN TIME PEOPLE SAY, "NEDDY, TELL ME HOW TO MAKE MY HALLOWEEN SPOOK-TER-DOODILY-RIFIC WITHOUT BREAKING THE MANY IMPORTANT SOCIAL AND ETHICAL MORES LAID DOWN FOR GOOD WHOLESOME FOLK-DIDDILY-OLK LIKE YOU AND ME." WELL, THE BIBLE DOESN'T SAY, "THOU SHALT NOT PARTY." SO HERE'S A LITTLE PRIMER I LIKE TO CALL...

HALLOWEEN HOEDOWN AT THE FLANDEROSA!

YAY! I'M CAUGHT IN LOVE'S GLORIOUS WEB!

MY LOST ISRAELITE'S GOT A WORM IN ITS BRAIN.

"SURE, BOBBING FOR APPLES IS FUN ENOUGH FOR MOST FOLK, BUT AT THE FLANDERS HUT, WE PREFER TO GO **BOBBING FOR THE LOST TRIBE OF ISRAEL!**"

"TRICK-OR-TREATERS MAY EXPECT AN IMPERSONAL HANDFUL OF CANDY, BUT AT THE FLANDERS HOME THE 'TREAT' IS A HUG AND THE GLIMMERING GLOW OF FRIENDSHIP."

WHA--?!

YEAH, WELL, I ALSO GOT THEIR BLENDER.

"PUMPKIN CARVING CAN BE FUN. WE HOLLOW THEM OUT TO MAKE DIORAMAS OF BIBLE SCENES. THEN WE GIVE THE PUMPKIN INNARDS TO PASSING TRANSIENTS AS A FREE GIFT."

HERE YA GO!

THANKS A HELLUVA LOT. I CAN NEITHER **SMOKE** NOR **DRINK** THIS.

"WHEN TELLING SCARY STORIES, IT'S ALWAYS GOOD TO TAKE 'SPECIAL' PRECAUTIONS FOR THE CHILDREN."

"WHEN IT COMES TO TRICKSTERS, I DON'T JUST TURN THE OTHER CHEEK, I TURN IT **ALL** THE WAY AROUND!"

"MAKE SURE YOUR CHILDREN KNOW WHAT COSTUMES THEIR FRIENDS WILL BE WEARING TO AVOID EXCESSIVE FEAR AND CONFUSION."

"IN FACT, MOST OF THE HALLOWEEN CAST OF CHARACTERS COULD USE A LITTLE RE-NEDUCATION. SOMETIMES JUST A NEW NAME CAN MAKE THEM MUCH MORE FLAN-DIDDILY-TASTIC..."

BOLTY, THE HUGGING GIANT

SAINT BONE-ABUS

LARRY THE WELL-LOVED LEPER

COMMUNION CHARLIE

"OF COURSE, EVEN AT THE FLANDERS PAD WE RECOGNIZE THERE SHOULD BE A LITTLE SCARE IN HALLOWEEN..."

THE CHAMBERMAID

"THE PERFECT CHAMBERMAID IS FEMININE, BUT IMPAIRED FROM SEEING THE MORE, SHALL WE SAY, 'DELICATE PARTICULARS' OF A GENTLEMAN'S ANATOMY."

HMM...

HELLO.

UH-OH, LOOKS LIKE WE HAVE SLUGS AGAIN.

THE LIBRARIAN

"TO MY WAY OF THINKING, A GOOD LIBRARIAN HAS A ROBUST HUNGER FOR GREAT BOOKS... AND HANDS TOO SMALL TO STEAL THEM."

ALAS, GONE ARE THE DAYS OF THE TWELVE BURRITO LUNCH.

THE JESTER

BRAAP!

WHOA! I DIDN'T WANT TO BE POINTED IN THAT DIRECTION!

"WHEN BUILDING A JESTER, FEEL FREE TO SHOW SOME ARTISTIC FLAIR... I DID."

THE GARDENER

"A GROUNDSKEEPER PLUS A POLITICIAN... THERE'S A MAN WHO KNOWS HIS WAY AROUND MANURE!"

ACH! I'M WEARIN' UNDER-PANTIES!!

THE LACKEY

"AS HE WAS THE ONLY ABLE-BODIED WORKER ON MY ENTIRE STAFF, I DECIDED TO CLONE SMITHERS... THEN CUT BOTH OF THEM IN HALF."

HELLO, HANDSOME.

"UNFORTUNATELY, HE BECAME A LITTLE TOO IN LOVE WITH HIMSELF."

THE CHEF

"THE MAN COOKING MY FOOD SHOULD HAVE A PUCKISH CREATIVITY COMBINED WITH A LOVE OF FOOD THAT KNOWS NO BOUNDS."

KNOWS NO BOUNDS, EH? KINDA LIKE HOMER'S GUT!

WHY YOU LITTLE--

ACHH! YACHH!

"OH, WELL, LOOKS LIKE I'LL BE EATING OUT."

AS AN EXPERT ON ALL THINGS HORRIFYING, I CAN SAFELY SAY THIS STORY WILL SCARE THE PANTS OFF OF YOU. AND IF THERE'S ONE OTHER THING I KNOW ABOUT, IT'S PANTSLESSNESS!

THE CURSE OF THE THING!
As told by ḃomer J. Simpson

When young ḃomer J. Simpson agreed to go on the beer-watching expedition deep in the heart of Beersylvania, he had no idea of the terror that would befall him on that fateful night.

Led by world-famous beer-keteer, Barney Gumble, the group had traveled by golly to the deepest part of oh, you know ... that state with the rednecks to find some beer. Coming around a bend, ḃomer spied an old man in a retirement home where he belongs. "Stay away from Monsterville, for that is the home of The Selmavore." ḃomer had heard this myth. Long ago, this fat chick named Selma had been been shaved, burlap-bagged, and thrown in the river by the church. Before she died, she swore her ghost would seek vengeance. Anyone she caught would be yammered at until their ears fell off. But ḃomer couldn't worry about myths. To find the beers, they had to go to Monsterland. As they left, they could hear the old man mutter, "I wish I'd left my son more money."

Because members of the group were scared, Barney agreed to sit up all night with his bomb machine. "ḃey look! I found a peanut in the dirt," he joked, "No really! I found a peanut!" Later that night, young ḃomer was awoken by gunshots followed by a hideous scream. He ran to the spot where Barney had been. Instead he found his dirt peanut and a moment later, he ate it. Suddenly, he heard a rustle in the bushes. THUMP, THUMP, SCRAPE... THUMP, THUMP, SCRAPE! Was it the Selmathing?! The guy... General whats-his-name began running back through the inky darkness toward the I have no idea what goes here. Once he reached it, he'd motor back to civilization and send for help. It seemed like an eternity, but he finally found it. His passage to safety! And as if that weren't enough, there on the plane ride home he could make out with the stewardess... He'd actually found all women love ḃomer the Great! But as he got closer, he realized Selma's butt was much bigger than he had imagined. Could it be Selma was actually stealing my pork rinds?

That morning in the MonsterTown Gazette there was a short article near the back: "Beetle Bailey Kisses Miss Buxley." An old man put down the paper and muttered to himself, "Why don't I ever shut up?"

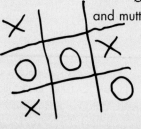

OH, MY! *THIS* LOOKS EXCITING!

AW C'MON, GRAMPA! YOU DON'T EXPECT ME TO BELIEVE YOU USED TO *PLAY* WITH THESE?

I DID. IT'S *TRUE!*

Call Me HOMER

JAUNDICED JEFF SMITH-STORY & BREAKDOWNS
MAD STEPHANIE GLADDEN-PENCILS
BILL "THE HORROR, THE HORROR" MORRISON-INKS
MIKE "MOJO" SAKAMOTO-LETTERING
NATHAN "RAISIN" KANE-COLORS
MATT "DR. PAIN" GROENING-SON OF BLUBBER

THE BOUVIER FAMILY ALBUM

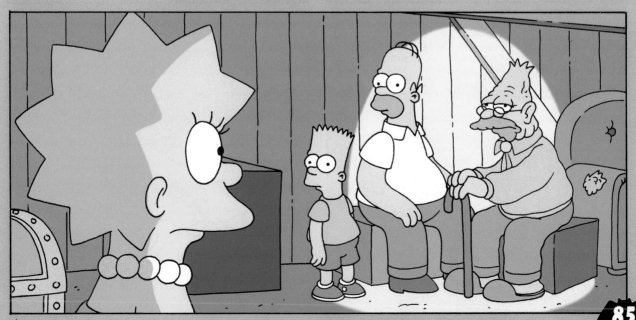

IT ALL STARTED ONE DAY AFTER A PARTICULARLY GOOD HARVEST OF WHALES...

YOUR GREAT, GREAT, GREAT, GREAT GRANDFATHER HOMER WAS IN CHARGE OF MELTING DOWN THE CHUNKS OF WHALE BLUBBER INTO OIL. HE RAN THE TRI-WORKS -- THE BIGGEST DEEP-FRYERS YOU EVER SAW!

C'MON! BRING ME MORE *BLUBBER*. I LOVE TO TURN STUFF INTO GREASE!

EVERYTHING WAS FINE UNTIL HOMER ACCIDENTALLY PUT HIS FINGER IN HIS MOUTH...

OOH! TASTY!

SMACK!

INSTANTLY HE DEVELOPED A TASTE FOR THE STUFF AND HAD TO GET BIGGER AND BIGGER DOSES TO SATISFY HIS CRAVINGS...

CHOMP!

MMM... BLUBBER.

WHAT'S ALL THAT CHOMPING NOISE COMING FROM THE HOLD?

IT'S TRI-WORKSMAN HOMER! AND HE JUST ATE MY 130TH% OF THE PROFITS!

CHOMP! CHOMP!

CAPTAIN BURNS! WHAT SHOULD WE *DO* WITH HIM?

TIE HIM TO *THE MAST!*

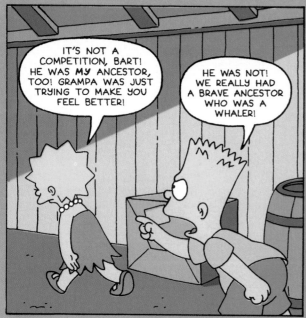

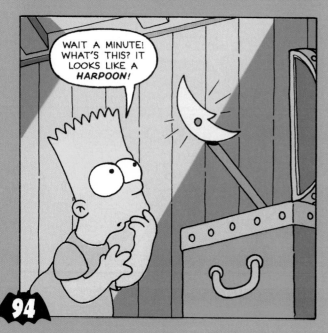

95

THE EVER-LOVIN' END!

BART SIMPSON – MASTER OF DISGUISE

presents

THE QUICK 'N' EASY, LOW-BUDGET DO-IT-YOURSELF GUIDE TO

COOL COSTUMES

MR. MARKER FACE

DOC LOOSE-LEAF, MAN OF PULP

THE HEADLESS GEEK

PROFESSOR PANTY HOSE

WALRUS MAN

CHOMP-ZILLA

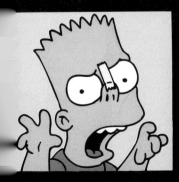

PHANTOM OF THE VIDEO ARCADE

THE MAN WHO COULD SEE HIS EYELIDS

VASELINO, THE THING THAT

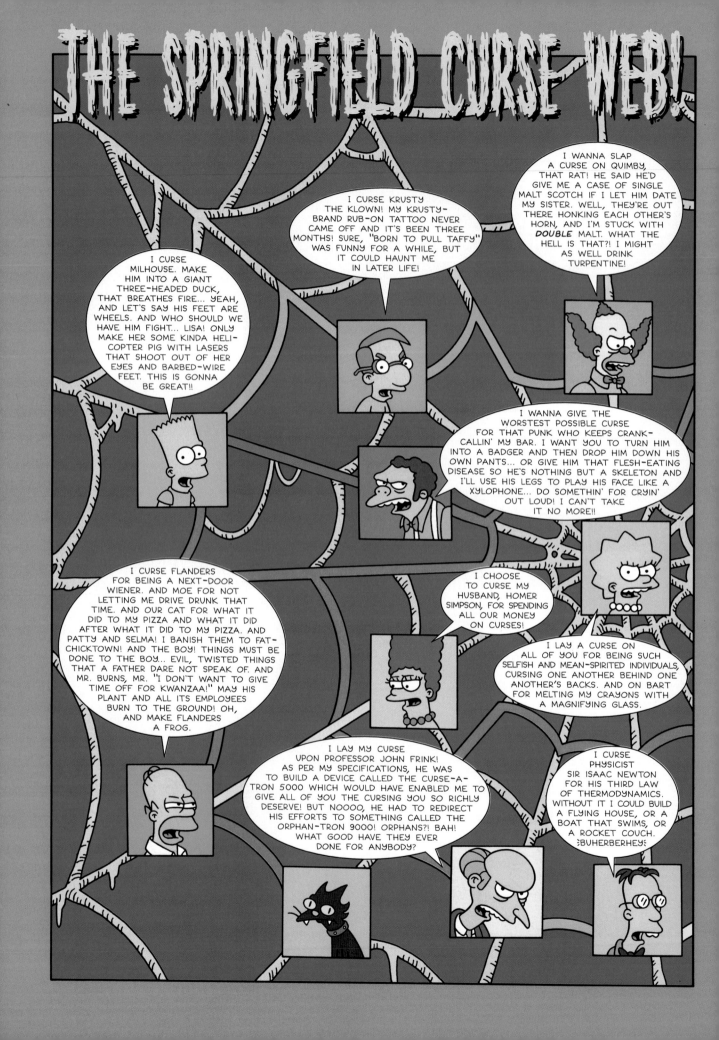

HALLOWEEN IS AN UGLY MELEE WHERE YOU'RE EITHER THE TREATED OR THE TRICKED. SO REMEMBER, WHEN YOU GO OUT ONTO THAT PUMPKIN-STREWN BATTLEFIELD, BE ALERT, BE PREPARED, AND WHEN NECESSARY, RUN LIKE HELL!

BART'S HALLOWEEN SURVIVAL KIT!

OH, THAT? JUST A LITTLE SOMETHING THE JOHNSONS ARE GIVING OUT. SAID THEY WERE MAKING UP FOR THEIR TIGHT-WAD NEIGHBORS.

TIGHTWAD?! I'LL SHOW THAT JOHNSO WHO THE TIGHTWAD JOAN! BRING THE BI CANDY BARS... HELL BRING THE VCR!

1 "AT FIRST, PEOPLE WILL WANT TO GIVE YOU SOME CANDY IN THE 'BITE-SIZED' FAMILY. BUT LOOK WHAT HAPPENS WHEN YOU 'ACCIDENTALLY' SHOW THEM WHAT THEIR NEIGHBORS ARE GIVING OUT."

THE LATEST ISSUE OF "DOILY PARADE!" AND IT'S SIGNED BY TONY RANDALL!

OF COURSE, I COULD JUST GRAB HIS BAG, BUT THEN, WHERE'S THE ART IN THAT?

"WHAT ARE THOSE EGGS DOING IN HERE... SURELY IT'S NOT EASTER?" ;WINK;

2 "THIS IS A LITTLE SOMETHING I CALL 'THE DORK DISTRACTER.'"

"EVERY SKINFLINT LOVES TO FIND SOMETHING IN THE MAILBOX. WHY NOT LET IT BE SHAVING CREAM?"

3 "WHEN IT COMES TO MAKING THE BIG CANDY HAUL, A COSTUME IS ONLY AS GOOD AS THE TEAR-JERKING STORY THAT GOES WITH IT."

4 "LET'S SAY YOU'RE GETTING CHASED BY... I DON'T KNOW, LET'S SAY THE POLICE. DONUTS MAKE A GREAT DIVERSION."

SEEING AS I ONLY HAVE THE ONE LEG AND THE ONE EYE, IT WAS THE ONLY COSTUME I COULD WEAR.

STOP, YA LITTLE HOODLUM! YA LITTLE EGG-THROWING, JELLY-FILLED, SPRINKLE-TOPPED... UM, COULD YA THROW SOME MILK?

YOU POOR THING! TAKE IT ALL!

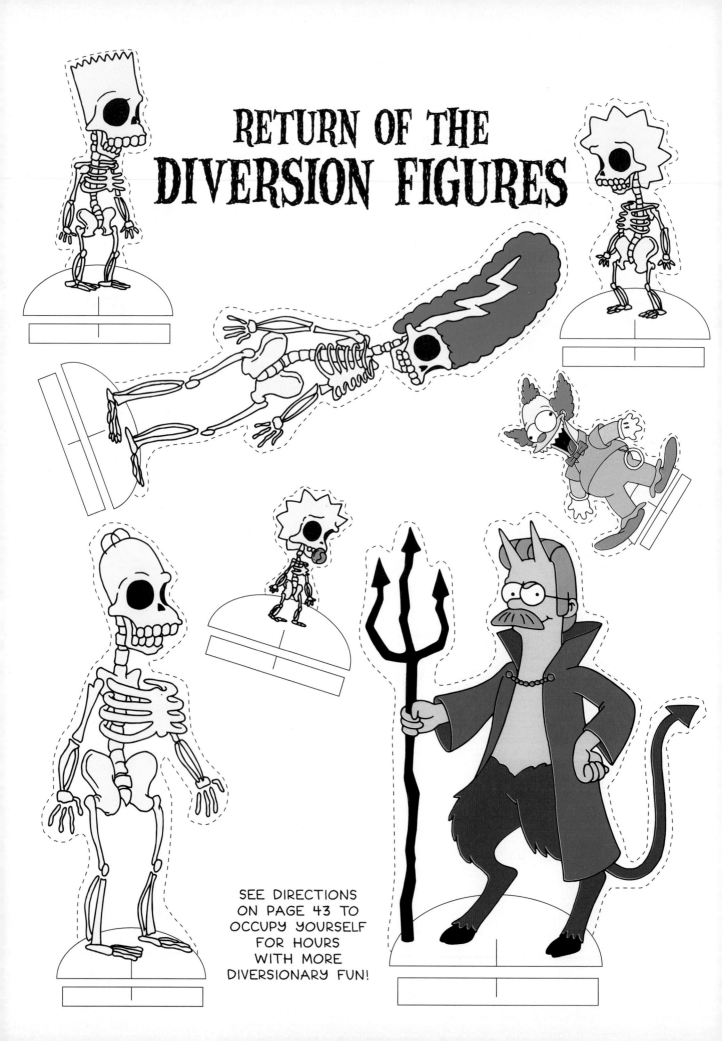

RETURN OF THE DIVERSION FIGURES

SEE DIRECTIONS ON PAGE 43 TO OCCUPY YOURSELF FOR HOURS WITH MORE DIVERSIONARY FUN!

BART PEOPLE

AHHH!

EEEK! CAT GIRL!

JAMES "GRAVE ROBBIN'"-SON: STORY
CHRIS "MOANIN' & GROANIN'" ROMAN: LAYOUTS
BILL "MORGUE"-ISON: FINISHED ART
MIKE "SHOCK"-AMOTO: LETTERING
CADAVEROUS NATHAN KANE: COLORS
MATT GRRRRROENING: TOP CAT

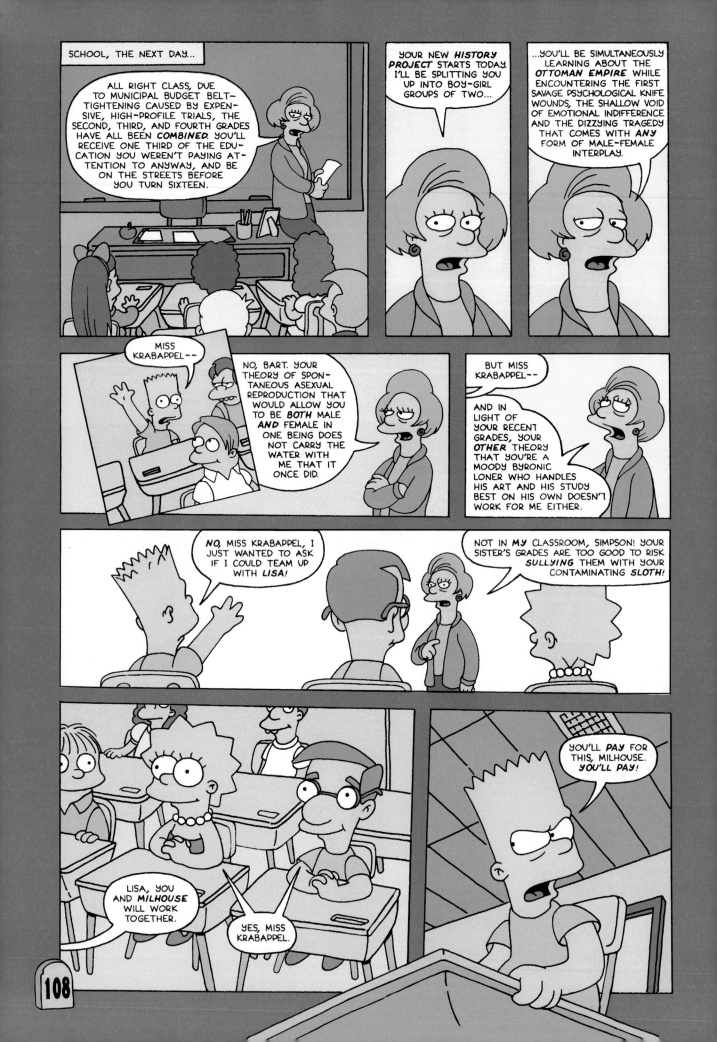

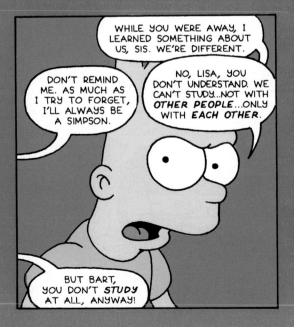

115

> YOU WANNA BE SCARED?! WELL, SHUT UP AND LISTEN, OR I'LL GIVE YOU SOMETHING TO BE SCARED *ABOUT!*

THE CURSE OF THE THING!

What's wrong with an old hero? Are you scared his teeth might fall out? So what if they do? It's my story and I'm makin' him a hero for the elderly

As told by _Abraham Simpson_.

When young _Ebeneezer M⁰Bride_ agreed to go on the _search for the scary monster_ deep in the heart of _the eeevil forest_, he had no idea of the terror that would befall him on that fateful night.

Led by world-famous _Dracula catcher, Dwight D. Eisenhow_, the group had traveled by _Edsel_ to the deepest part of _the eee evil forrest_ to find well, something evil, ya dunderhead. Coming around a bend, ~~something stupid~~ _Ebeneezer_ spied well, not in an old man ~~I bet you think the~~ old man is going to say. "Stay away from _The Castle of the Mole People_, for my story! that is the home of _the eeevil Mole Princess_." _Ebeneezer_ had heard this myth. Long ago, _You might not think_ had been _moles are scary, but in my day they were everywhere!_ by a rival _____. Before he died, he swore his ghost would seek vengeance. Anyone he caught would be fed to the moles, I tell ya ~~as he was~~. But _Ebeneezer_ couldn't worry about myths. To find the _Eeevil Mole Princess_, they had to go to _find her_. As they left, they could hear the ~~old~~ smart man mutter, "_If yer not scared a moles by now, wait till Easter!_"

Because members of the group were scared, _Ebeneezer_ agreed to sit up all night with _his achin' back and bowel troubles_. My bowels are nothin to joke about! he joked, "_I said it's nothing to joke about!_" Later that night, young _Dadburnit_ was awoken by gunshots followed by a hideous scream. He ran to the spot where _Chachi_ had been. Instead he found his _Fonzie's dog_ and a _Nuts to this! I'm goin fer a malted!_. Suddenly, he heard a rustle in the bushes. THUMP, THUMP, SCRAPE... THUMP, THUMP, SCRAPE! Was it _____?! _____ began running back through the inky darkness toward _____. Once he reached it, he'd motor back to civilization and send for help. It seemed like an eternity, but he finally found it. His passage to safety! And as if that weren't enough, there _____ he could make out _Im back. What'd I miss?_ He'd actually found _Where the hell are the Mole People you mentioned?_! But as he got closer, he realized _This story stinks!_ was much bigger than he had imagined. Could it be _I could write a better story with a bag around my head_ was actually _____ _Blah, blah, blah, who cares?_?

That morning in the _____ Gazette there was a short article near the back: "_____." An old man put down the paper and muttered to himself, "_Im back! What'd I_ miss?

When people would ask, "How'd ya sleep?" you'd say, "Moley" or "Not so Moley." And at Easter, our parents wouldn't hide eggs, they'd hide moles. "Ah! I wish I hadn't found a mole!" You'd yell as one bit you on the finger. Easter was a hoooooorible time!

Why can't ya accept an old hero?! I'll tell ya why! Cuz this story thing was probably put together by those senior haters over at Young Miss magazine! For shaaame! I've read your magazine. All you young people care about is soda pop, flavored lipsticks and that guy Chachi! Chachi, Chachi, Chachi! You think old people don't know Chachi, but we do! He's Fonzie's son, or his dog. And he sickens us! Some day old people will rule the world, and then you'll be sorry. Sincerely, Abraham Simpson P.S. I loved you in "All about Eve".

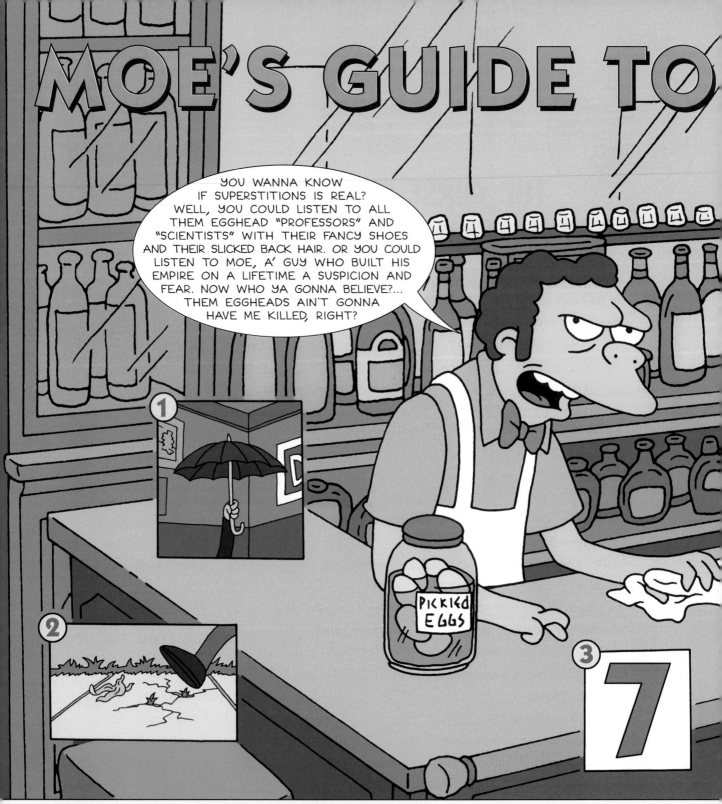

1. **IT'S BAD LUCK TO OPEN AN UMBRELLA INDOORS.**
"LET'S SEE... THERE WAS THE TIME MY BOOKIE SHOWED UP, AND I DIDN'T HAVE THE MONEY, AND ONE A' HIS BOYS USED AN UMBRELLA ON ME. THAT UMBRELLA GOT OPENED INDOORS, ALRIGHT, A LITTLE TOO INDOORS IF YA GET MY DRIFT. ≡SIGH≡ IF THAT AIN'T BAD LUCK, I DON'T KNOW WHAT IS."

2. **STEP ON A CRACK, BREAK YOUR MOTHER'S BACK.**
"UNFORTUNATELY, THIS ONE AIN'T TRUE. LORD KNOWS I'VE TRIED."

3. **THE NUMBER SEVEN WILL BRING GOOD FORTUNE.**
"DAMN RIGHT IT WILL. THAT'S WHY I MAKE SURE THERE'S ONLY SEVEN PEANUTS IN THE NUT TRAY, SEVEN SQUARES A' T.P. IN EACH JOHN, AND I CHARGE SEVEN BUCKS FOR MARGARITAS. THAT AIN'T BEIN' CHEAP, THAT'S TO BRING YOU GOOD LUCK, YA BUM!"

4. **THIRTEEN IS AN UNLUCKY NUMBER.**
"ALLS I KNOW IS, IF BARNEY'S HAD THIRTEEN BEERS AND THE BATHROOM'S OUTTA ORDER, THERE AIN'T NO GOOD LUCK FOR NO ONE."

5. **IF A BLACK CAT CROSSES YOUR PATH, IT'S BAD LUCK FOR THE REST OF THE WEEK.**
"THIS ONE'S TRUE. ONE DAY A BLACK CAT CROSSED RIGHT IN FRONTA ME. THAT VERY NIGHT, I TAKE MY GIRLFRIEND OUT

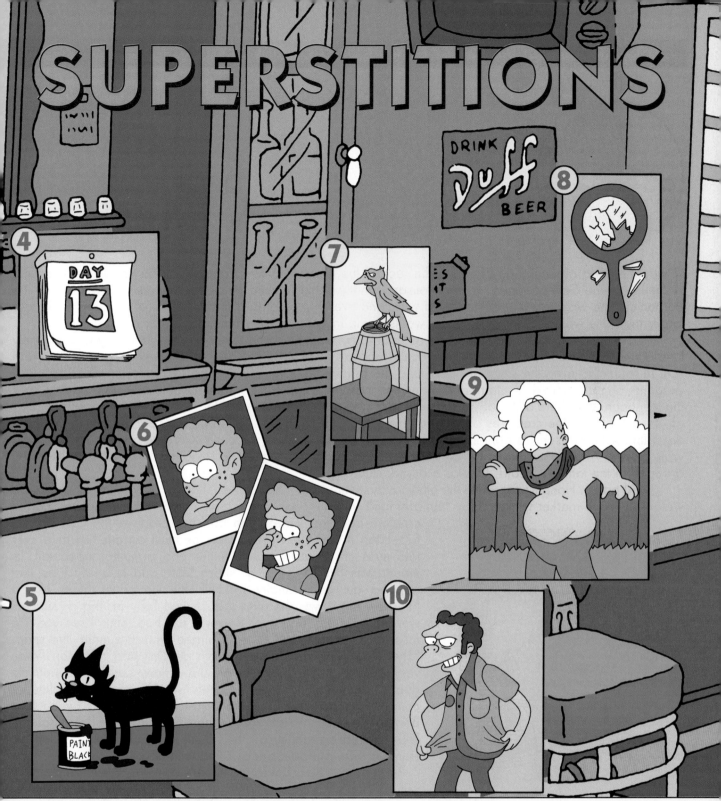

SUPERSTITIONS

"FOR OUR ANNIVERSARY, AND SHE BREAKS UP WITH ME. SAID I WASN'T CLASSY ENOUGH! RIGHT THERE IN FRONTA ALL MY FRIENDS AT THE STRIP CLUB! YEAH, THE CAT'S THE ONLY EXPLANATION ON THAT ONE."

6. IF YOU MAKE A FACE LONG ENOUGH, IT WILL STAY THAT WAY.
"THIS ONE'S HAUNTED ME EVER SINCE KINDYGARTEN."

7. A BIRD IN THE HOUSE IS A SIGN OF DEATH.
"ONLY IF THE HEALTH INSPECTOR SHOWS UP. AND, OF COURSE, HE'S GONNA SHOW. UP! HE ALWAYS SHOWS UP! I MEAN, WHADDAS HE LIVE NEXT DOOR?!"

8. A BROKEN MIRROR IS SEVEN YEARS' BAD LUCK.
"THE BAD LUCK WAS HAVING 'FREE HAMMER NIGHT' IN THE FIRST PLACE."

9. IF YOU EAT A WATERMELON SEED, IT WILL GROW A WATERMELON IN YOUR STOMACH.
"THIS ONE AIN'T TRUE, ALTHOUGH I AIN'T SURE ABOUT MY PICKLED EGGS. LET'S JUST SAY I'M MENTIONED IN A LAWSUIT."

10. WEAR THE SAME SHIRT AND IT WILL BRING YOU GOOD LUCK.
"OH, I GOT A LUCKY SHIRT. AND IF I WEAR IT ON A FRIDAY NIGHT, I GET LUCKY ALRIGHT, **REAL** LUCKY! HEH, HEH, HEH... AAAAH, WHO'M I KIDDING. I STILL END UP AT HOME WATCHING A SCRAMBLED VERSION A' THE NUDIE CHANNEL."

"YE LANDLUBBERS KNOW THE SEA AS A PLACE OF FROLIC AND WHIMSY. A PLACE TO DIP YOUR WEE ANKLES IN THE HOT SUMMER MONTHS, AND WHERE THE WORST THAT CAN HAPPEN IS SAND CRABS IN YOUR BATHIN' PANTIES. ARRGH, BUT THAT BE IN THE SHALLOWS. FOR DEEP IN THE BELLY OF THE BEAST, WHERE LIGHT HAS NO NAME AND SOUND IS NAUGHT BUT THE SLOW SCREAM OF DEATH, LIVE CREATURES SO FOUL, SO HIDEOUS THAT TO MERELY SPEAK THEIR NAME IS TO DIE OF FRIGHT. TRULY, YOU DON'T WANT THESE CREATURES EVEN NEAR YOUR PANTIES. WHAT FOLLOWS IS THE HORRIFYIN' ACCOUNT OF JUST SUCH A BEAST."

The Trench Wraith

'Twas the dead of winter, and I was sailin' across the North Pacific as captain of the good ship *Gertrude Stein*. Ah, the *Gertrude Stein*... a two-thousand-ton lily of the sea, dainty as her namesake and with half the barnacles. She was truly a ship that could withstand even the greatest danger. But we'd soon find a danger larger than any we could imagine, and it would come from the smallest member of our crew.

Little Tobias Trivel had signed on as cabin boy, and the crew loved him in the way you could only love a small person. His tiny, little hands could reach in to fix whirring gears, he could be greased up and sent in to unclog even the smallest pipes, and the fishermen in the crew found he made excellent bait. Just drag him on a rope from the stern, and within seconds you'd be reelin' in a marlin the size of a couch. Crack the fish open, and there'd be Toby, covered in fish goo and smilin' big as life. Yes, he was a stupid boy, but, oh, how he loved the creatures of the sea! He loved 'em so much, he turned his quarters into a veritable aquarium with rare species from the four corners of the globe. Why, he even swore he had a fish that could write poetry. And it may have, for all we know. If only it hadn't been electrocuted by the typewriter Toby dropped in the tank. As I said, he was a stupid, stupid boy.

At port in Hong Kong, while the other sailors were hittin' the brothels, fightin' in bars, and buyin' their weight in black market wicker, Toby found himself in a tiny exotic fish store filled with every rare marine

creature from the Venezuelan dancin' scrod, to the East Borneo face-biter. It was there Toby spied the most curious fish he'd ever laid eyes on. It had flipper-like fins and a multipronged tail. Its mouth was filled with long, sharp teeth and a bristly tube that popped out occasionally to suck the aquarium glass like a lamprey. But it was the eyes that sucked Toby in. Big as saucers were they, puppy dog eyes if ever a fish had 'em. "I see you like most rare," said the wizened Chinese woman runnin' the shop. "That legendary trench wraith from deepest part of ocean. Very, very dangerous. If you take on ship, many sailors die horrible death." But young Toby hadn't been listenin', and the shopkeeper couldn't repeat herself, as she'd just been attacked by an East Borneo face-biter. While the woman wrestled with her assailant, Toby placed his money on the counter and unknowingly, left the store carryin' a plastic baggy filled with doom.

But a scary little fish was the future's concern. We were ten days out of Hong Kong and jammed to the hatches with the most important cargo we'd ever carried: the entire spring line for the Paris Women's Fashion Show. To reach France in time, we would have to sail as quickly as possible through some of the most treacherous waters on earth. But I knew my crew, and they were hearty. I gathered the men on deck and announced, "We'll make our deadline so long as we work hard, stay alert, and, most importantly, no matter how strong the allure, no one, but no one tries on those dresses." Then, to prove I was serious, I banished Bosun Hale to the brig just for sneaking on a pair of Donna Karan thigh-highs.

Ladies stockings were not on young Toby's mind, however. Down in his quarters he stared with fascination as the fish he had interestin'ly named Colonel Sucky Mouth began to glow a bright green, and its puppy dog eyes began pulsatin' in their sockets. The other fish swam nervously to the other side of the tank, for fish are always the first to smell danger. Suddenly, the exotic fish emitted a loud throbbin' squeal that seemed to carry out over the sea itself. Up on deck, the lookout rubbed his eyes then looked again. Had he really just seen that strange, dark shape pass under the bow of the boat? Little did he know that a monster had been summoned from the murky depths.

That night, as the ship's bell rang out eleven o'clock, the first victim was claimed. The evening to that point had been calm, relaxing even. Most of the men had gathered in the conference hall to watch our musical society's production of "Grease." A production, I might add, for which I received great acclaim in the role of Rizzo. But the magic of that marvelous play was rent asunder when Ensign Goldner burst in and announced that the cook was dead. We rushed to the kitchen. At first all we could see was the spigot of the sink runnin' as if someone were washin' vegetables. But next to the sink was a sight most unappetizin'. There, lying on the floor, was the body of our beloved cook, sucked dry like a shriveled raisin. Nothin' left of him but skin, bones, and an Anna Sui strapless evening gown. What beastly creature could do such a thing?! Back in Toby's quarters, Colonel Sucky Mouth continued his siren call.

The next mornin' we searched for the cook's murderer. The bravest men searched the kitchen, while the less brave agreed to look around their rooms and in their pants pockets. One particularly cowardly party decided they better take the ship's helicopter and search some of those brothels back in Hong Kong. But no one found the creature. What was found instead was the body of Xavier McDaniels, shriveled bone dry despite being found in the shower, and the equally desiccated body of the ship's bilge operator Flowers O'Dooley. Fear gripped the sailors. Weeks from land, bein' attacked by an unknowable assailant, and not to mention completely lost. (I'd locked the navigator in the brig three days earlier for wearing culottes after Labor Day.) I had to find that creature, but how? That's when it hit me like a mizzenmast: the shower, the bilge pump, the kitchen sink... the creature was attackin' from the water supply!

Slowly, I lifted the hatch to the ship's giant water tank and peered inside. What I saw shivered every part of me timbers. 'Twas the female trench wraith, ghastly and huge, with teeth like swords and a mouth tube like a fire hose. Aye, she was the female, for all around her, attached to the sides of the tank, were large egg sacs, waitin' to be fertilized with the souls of our crew. With a shriek, the beast was upon me. Crashin' through the water tank, it flopped across the deck after me at an astounding pace. Arrgh, and I may have escaped, had I not been tryin' to outrun a demon in my Versace micro-mini and beige slingbacks by Nine West. With me backed against a wall, the trench wraith's evil suckin' tube began probing my neck, looking for the easiest access to my very soul. Suddenly, a voice came from the ship's rail, "Why settle for ground chuck when you can have filet mignon!" It was Toby! The suckin' tube slowly turned, sniffin' at the air until it pointed at Toby. "This is my fault! And now only I can save the ship!" I've said it before, and I'll say it again, that boy sure made excellent bait. In a shot, the wraith was upon Toby, suckin' his soul for all it was worth. But it was too late, Toby leapt off the rail with all his might, carryin' himself and the trench wraith into the churnin' waves below. As Toby fell, we could hear him yell, "Take care of Colonel Sucky Moooooouuuuthhh!" Yes, he was a stupid, stupid boy.

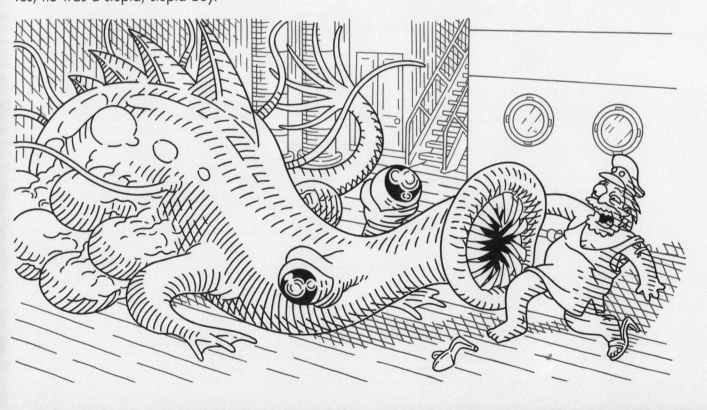

When the weather outside is frightful, their tones are so delightful.

Perry Kodos and Nat Kang Cole's
Yuletide Sing-Along

Perry Kodos recounts his holiday memories...

"Growing up as young larvae in the exotic land of...Ottawa, my sister and I never celebrated what you call 'Christmas.' However, it is remarkably similar to Lord Ozrap's Twelve Days of Terror, a cherished Ottawa tradition. While you have a red-suited man who enters your home spreading joy, our red-suited man spreads a skin-searing paste. You gather in groups to sing songs of what you call "love and friendship." We gather in groups to defend against Ozrap's throat-nesting wasp minions. The similarities are many. Thus we have recorded this holiday disc in the name of understanding between two cultures. Imagine how much smoother the assimilation will be when one of those cultures decides to violently overthrow and enslave the other. It is our holiday gift to you."

Including These Holiday Favorites:

"All Hail the Electronic Tree"
"Mouth Fight Under the Mistletoe"
"Here's Your Gift, Now What's For Me"
"Ding, Ding, Dong, Eliminate the Weak"
"I Saw Mommy Kiss a Replicant"

"Santa Kang Will Fill Your Socks"
"The Fruitcake Claims a Victim"
"It Is Time to Be Re-Nogged"
"An Obese Man Invaded My Soot Pipe"
"Hush Little Infant, You'll Make a Worthy Slave"

LITTLE SHOP OF HOMERS

MIKE ALL-DEAD
STORY & INKS

LUIS ESCOBAR
SINISTER
BREAKDOWNS

BILL "SON OF
GODZILLA" MORRISON
PENCILS

MIKE "HEAD ON
PIKE" SAKAMOTO
LETTERING

LAURA ALL-BLED &
NATHAN "KILLER" KANE
COLORS

MOTLEY MATT
GROENING
MR. GREENJEANS

ON A TYPICAL EVENING AT THE SIMPSON HOUSE...

THIS BLOWS! THESE DON'T EVEN WORK ON A MAGAZINE. THE ONLY SENSATION I'M GETTING IS A *THROBBING HEADACHE!*

HEY HOMER, WHOEVER SOLD YOU THESE X-RAY SPECS RIPPED YOU OFF. IN FACT, I SUGGEST WE CONSIDER A LAWSUIT. I THINK I'M GETTING A *BRAIN TUMOR!*

DON'T BE SILLY, BART. THE WARRANTY ON THOSE TOP-SECRET GOGGLES MUST HAVE EXPIRED *YEARS* AGO.

SNIP!

SNIP!

AYE CARUMBA! THEY *DO* WORK! THIS IS DISGUSTING! AT LEAST WHOEVER DE-SIGNED THIS TECHNO-LOGY HAD THE GOOD TASTE TO PUT A LIMIT ON WHAT THESE GLASSES CAN REVEAL!

OH, MY MISTAKE. I WAS RIGHT THE FIRST TIME...*JUNK!*

SPEAKING OF DISGUSTING, WHAT'S THAT *AWFUL SMELL?*

OH *DAD!* YOU KNOW A FEW DISCOMFORTS ARE SOMETIMES REQUIRED IN THE QUEST FOR SCIENTIFIC SATISFACTION.

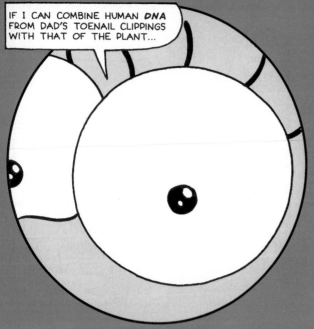

THE NEXT MORNING...

LISA, HONEY, TIME TO GET UP AND GET READY FOR SCHOOL!

HOW CAN YOU STAND THAT STENCH, SWEETIE? IT'S *HORRIBLE*. I WANT YOU TO THROW OUT THAT PLANT.

MMMM. MOM, I *CAN'T*. IT'S MY *SCIENCE PROJECT*.

I HATE TO *TELL* YOU THIS, LISA. BUT I THINK YOUR SCIENCE PROJECT IS NO LONGER WITH US.

ON NO! WHY? WHY? WHY?

DEAR, SWEET PLANT, I HAD HOPED TO GIVE YOU MORE THAN A LIFE OF FLIES AND MANURE. BUT, ALAS, 'TWAS NOT MEANT TO BE. ⸬SNIFF SNIFF⸬

MMMMMM...

BUMMER, HUH, SIS?

THIS WILL MAKE AN EXCELLENT *STINK BOMB!*

131

ON THE WAY TO A RUN-OF-THE-MILL *MELTDOWN* STORY AT THE SPRINGFIELD NUCLEAR PLANT, I WAS FORTUNATE ENOUGH TO RUN ACROSS THE FOLLOWING EXCITING STORY...

BART SIMPSON, A BOY GENIUS AND HORTICULTURIST EXTRAORDINAIRE, INTRODUCED HIS LATEST SUCCESS AT APU NAHASAPEEMAPETILON'S KWIK-E-MART AND PLANT SHOP -- AN INCREDIBLE *DONUT-EATING PLANT.*

MMMMMM, DONUTS.

GRRRRRRR...

HEY EVERYBODY, HAVE YOU SEEN THE NEWS?! I'VE GOT A SWELL NEW JOB! I SELL DONUTS AT APU'S FOR PEOPLE TO FEED THE PLANT THAT LISA...

BART YOU CONSCIENCELESS BETRAYER! YOU TOLD EVERYONE THAT *YOU* CREATED THAT PLANT.

RELAX, SIS. I'M GONNA CUT YOU IN ON THE ACTION. HERE, TAKE SOME *MOOLAH.*

GRRRRR!

135

Cover Art to *Treehouse of Horror* #1

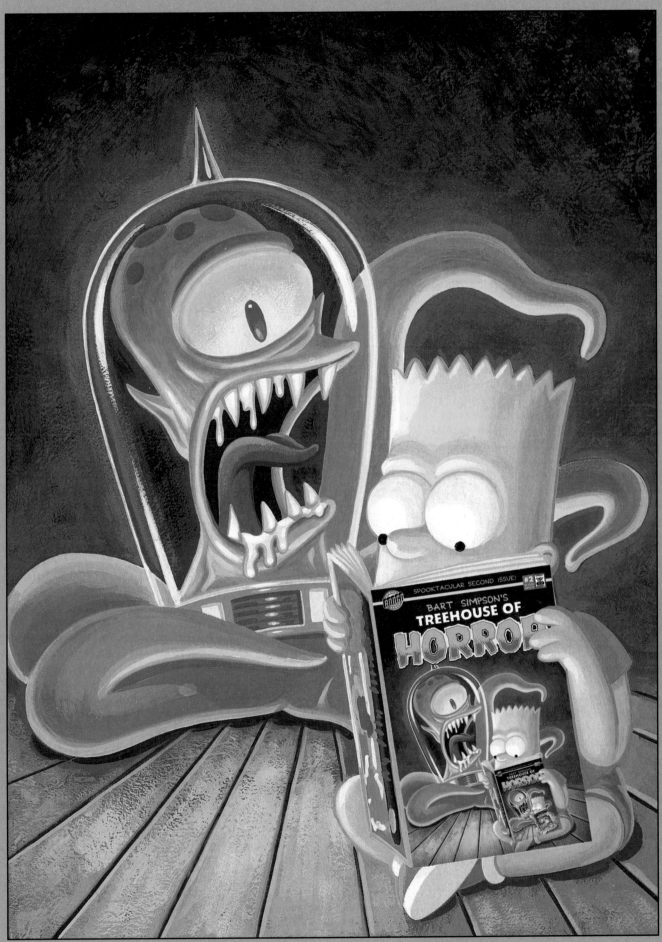

Cover Art to *Treehouse of Horror* #2

Cover Art to *Treehouse of Horror* #3